The publisher acknowledges the support of the Government of Canada, Department of
Canadian Heritage, Book Publishing Industry Development Program.

ISBN 1-55082-299-3

Design by Sari Naworynski.

Printed and bound in Canada by Champlain Graphics, Pickering, Ontario.

Published by Quarry Press Inc., 1180 Medical Court, Suite A, Carmel, Indiana 46032
and 195 Allstate Parkway, Markham, Ontario L3R 4T8.

QUARRY
HERITAGE

BOOKS

THE
Star
Spangled
BANNER

Lyrics by Francis Scott Key

Illustrations by Susan Winget

Sung by Lee Greenwood

O say, can you see, by the dawn's early light,
What so proudly we hailed at the twilight's last gleaming?

Whose broad stripes and bright stars, through the perilous fight,

O'er the ramparts we watched, were so gallantly streaming?

OLD GLORY

And the rockets' red glare, the bombs bursting in air,
Gave proof through the night that our flag was still there.

O say, does that star-spangled banner yet wave
O'er the land of the free and the home of the brave?

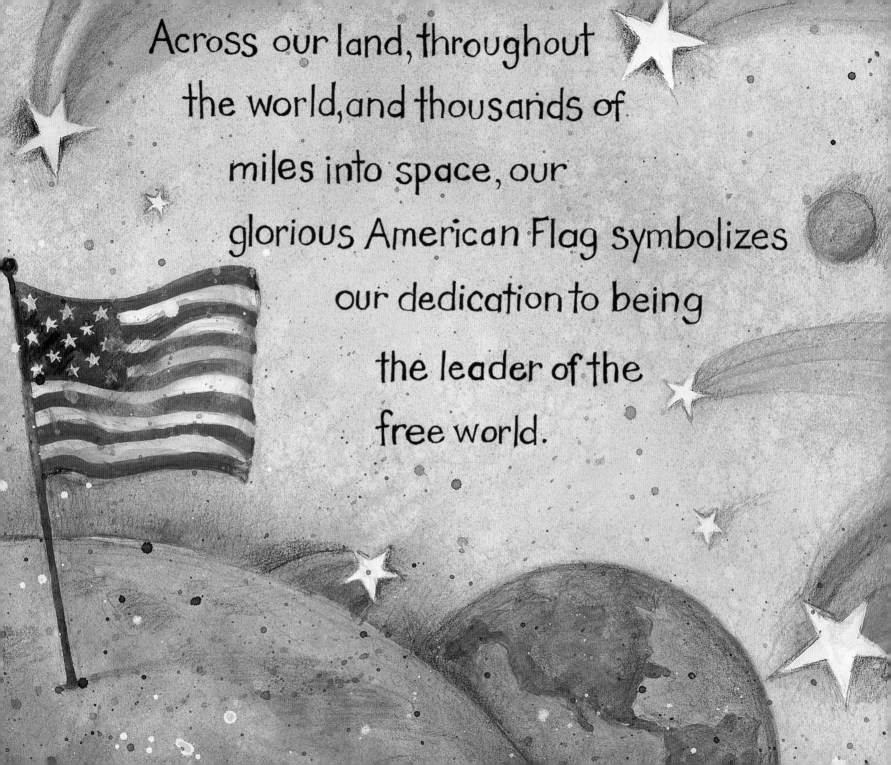

Across our land, throughout the world, and thousands of miles into space, our glorious American Flag symbolizes our dedication to being the leader of the free world.

On the shore dimly seen through the mists of the deep,
Where the foe's haughty host in dread silence reposes,
What is that which the breeze, o'er the towering steep,
As it fitfully blows, half conceals, half discloses?

Now it catches the gleam of the morning's first beam,
In full glory reflected, now shines on the stream:
'Tis the star-spangled banner: O, long may it wave
O'er the land of the free and the home of the brave!

Then conquer we must, for our cause it is just,
And this be our motto: "In God is our trust"
And the star-spangled banner in triumph shall wave
O'er the land of the free and the home of the brave!

And where is that band who so vauntingly swore
That the havoc of war and the battle's confusion
A home and a country should leave us no more?
Their blood has washed out their foul footsteps' pollution.

No refuge could save the hireling and slave
From the terror of flight or the gloom of the grave:
And the star-spangled banner in triumph doth wave
O'er the land of the free and the home of the brave.

Land of the Free

Home of the Brave

Oh, thus be it ever when freemen shall stand,
Between their loved homes and the war's desolation!
Blest with victory and peace, may the heaven-rescued land
Praise the Power that hath made and preserved us as a nation.

THE STORY OF THE SONG

The Star Spangled Banner was written by Francis Scott Key during the War of 1812, just after the British had sacked Washington and laid siege to Fort McHenry near Baltimore. A legal advisor to the American army, Francis Scott Key boarded a British ship under a flag of truce in Chesapeake Bay to negotiate the release of an American prisoner of war. He was detained overnight during the shelling of Fort McHenry. Despite a fierce bombardment of the fort, the Americans were able to rebuff the British. The next morning, Francis Scott Key was delighted to see the 'Stars and Stripes' flag flying above the ramparts. Our flag was still there! He took a letter from his pocket and wrote a poem on the back to commemorate the occasion.

OLD GLORY

Flag of the brave

thy folds shall fly

The sign of hope and triumph high.

OLD GLORY

Joseph Rodman Drake

First published in September 1814 under the title "Defense of Fort M'Henry," the poem soon became a popular patriotic song when renamed *The Star Spangled Banner* and set to the resounding music of "To Anacreon in Heaven." In 1931, *The Star Spangled Banner* was proclaimed the Official National Anthem of the United States of America by President Herbert Hoover.

The flag Francis Scott Key saw flying at Fort McHenry is now preserved at the Smithsonian Institution in Washington, DC. Sewn according to the basic design created by Francis Hopkinson and Betsy Ross for the Continental Congress in 1774, this flag features 15 stars and 15 stripes, as specified in 1794 by an Act of Congress. In 1818, Congress reduced the number of stripes to 13, but allowed a star for each state.

Stars and Stripes

Forever

Sometimes called "Star and Stripes" and other times "The Star Spangled Banner," this flag has become the symbol of the nation. "I pledge allegiance to the Flag of the United States of America and the Republic for which it stands," Americans proudly proclaim: "one Nation under God, indivisible, with Liberty and Justice for all." The flag is flown on all national holidays, including Memorial Day, Independence Day, and National Flag Day.

The American flag has been affectionately called "Old Glory" since the 1830s when sea captain Stephen Driver first exclaimed these words as the flag was unfurled. Captain Driver was among the crew who had rescued the infamous mutineers from *The Bounty*. During the Civil War, he hid his flag inside his bedcover from Rebel forces in Nashville until he was able to fly "Old Glory" again after the Union victory.

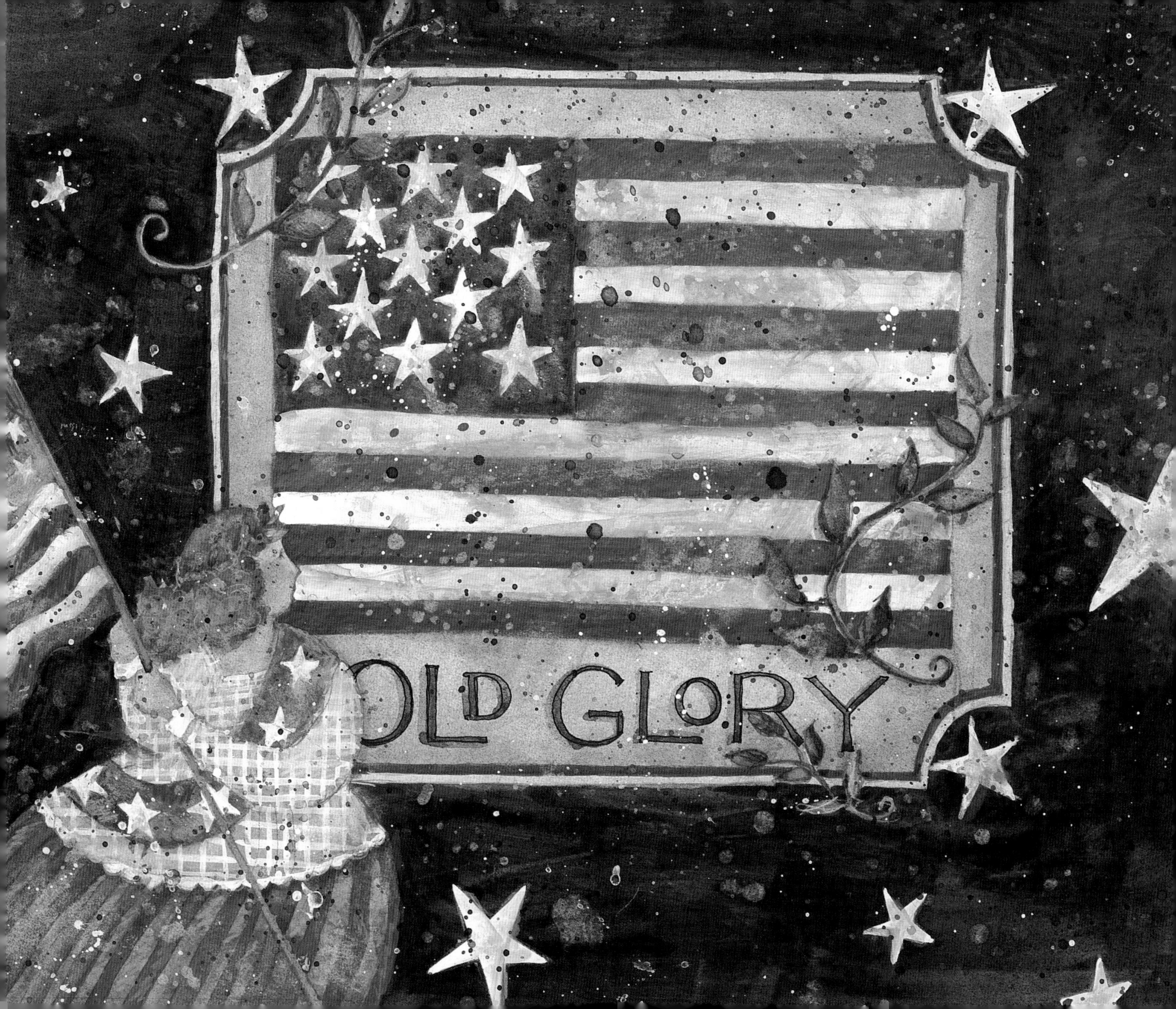
OLD GLORY

The Star Spangled Banner became the inspiration for another popular patriotic song when John Philip Sousa composed *The Stars and Stripes Forever*, now the Official March of the United States of America.

For more information on Francis Scott Key and *The Star Spangled Banner*, contact the Library of Congress on the Internet at www.loc.gov, the University of Oklahoma Law Center at www.law.ou.edu, and the Smithsonian Institution at www.si.edu. For the Pledge of Allegiance, visit www.usflag.org; for Old Glory, visit www.usflag.org; for *The Stars and Stripes Forever*, visit www.dws.org.sousa.